INSPIRE

HAIR FASHION FOR SALON CLIENTS

Goldwell Switch Collection Team — HAIR: Rush London • MAKE-UP: Goldwell Switch Collection Team

INSPIRE

HAIR FASHION FOR SALON CLIENTS

Featuring
Sophisticated Styles

TABLE OF CONTENTS VOL. 62

Sempre Bellezza-
Temecula CA
HAIR: Shana Sohner
MAKE-UP: Sara Wayne
PHOTO: Taggart Winterhalter
for Purely Visual

3

Van Michael Salons
HAIR: Van Michael Salon Team
PHOTO: Babak
*Courtesy of NAHA

Joe's Salon & Spa
HAIR: Charleen McILVenny Koval
COLOR: Charleen McILVenny Koval
MAKE-UP: Sarah Griswold
PHOTO: John Kane

Carter T. Lund & Associates
HAIR: Carter T. Lund
MAKE-UP: Sara Wayne
PHOTO: Taggart Winterhalter
for Purely Visual

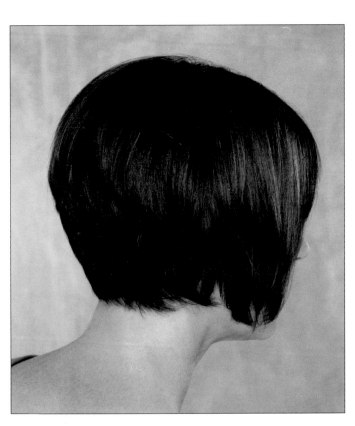

Carter T. Lund & Associates
HAIR: Carter T. Lund
MAKE-UP: Sara Wayne
PHOTO: Taggart Winterhalter
for Purely Visual

**Michael's Salon
& Day Spa**
HAIR: Jodi Schuh-Keeley
COLOR: Jodi Schuh-Keeley
MAKE-UP: Fawn/Mac
PHOTO: Scott Bryant

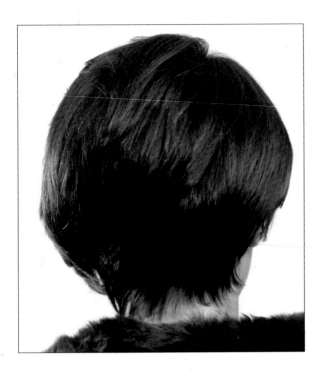

Edie's Styling Center
HAIR: Rachel Woolums
COLOR: Edie' Noppenberger
MAKE-UP: Rachel Woolums
PHOTO: Scott Bryant

Edie's Styling Center
HAIR: Edie' Noppenberger
COLOR: Edie' Noppenberger
MAKE-UP: Fawn/Mac
PHOTO: Scott Bryant

Hair Benders Internationalé
HAIR: Hair Benders Design Team
COLOR: Hair Benders Design Team
MAKE-UP: Darin Wright
PHOTO: Scott Bryant

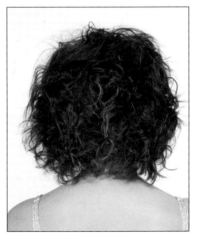

Kathy Adams Salon
HAIR: Kathy Adams Salon Team
MAKE-UP: Kathy Adams Salon Team
PHOTO: Tom Carson Photography

HAIR: Shortino's Salon & Spa Team
MAKE-UP: Shortino's Salon & Spa Team
PHOTO: Tom Carson Photography

T.Carltons Studio
HAIR: Donna Pappas
MAKE-UP: Noelle Guidice
PHOTO: Larry Hacken

The Cutting Room Hair Design
HAIR: The Cutting Room Hair Design Team
PHOTO: Babak
*Courtesy of NAHA

Shortino's Salon & Spa
HAIR: Shortino's Salon & Spa Team
MAKE-UP: Shortino's Salon & Spa Team
PHOTO: Tom Carson Photography

Pivot Point International
HAIR: Pivot Point International Artistic Team
MAKE-UP: Lori Neapolitan
PHOTO: Mike van den Toom/David Placek

Kathy Adams Salon
HAIR: Kathy Adams Salon Team
MAKE-UP: Kathy Adams Salon Team
PHOTO: Tom Carson Photography

**John Amico Haircare & Jalyd Haircolor-
Stardust Beauty Salon**
HAIR: Kathy Canfield
MAKE-UP: Kathy Canfield
PHOTO: Scott Bryant

14

Diadema Hair Fashion
HAIR: Diadema
MAKE-UP: Tiziana Romano for Diadema
PHOTO: Stefano Bidini

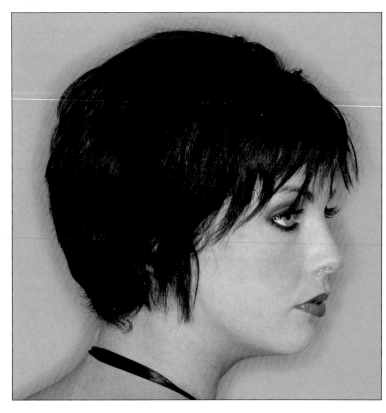

Sempre Bellezza Salon-Temecula CA
HAIR: Daniella Del Fante
MAKE-UP: Jaime Queenin
PHOTO: Taggart Winterhalter
for Purely Visual

16

Fantastic Sams-Irvine CA
HAIR: Jennifer Metzger
PHOTO: Taggart Winterhalter
for Purely Visual

Kathy Adams Salon
HAIR: Kathy Adams Salon Team
MAKE-UP: Kathy Adams Salon Team
PHOTO: Tom Carson Photography

Goldwell Trend Zoom
HAIR: Goldwell Trend Zoom Team
MAKE-UP: Goldwell Trend Zoom Team
PHOTO: Courtesy of Goldwell

Gina Khan Salon
HAIR: Gina Khan
MAKE-UP: Dino
PHOTO: Vijai Manilal

Van Michael Salons
HAIR: Van Michael Salon Team
PHOTO: Babak
*Courtesy of NAHA

Goldwell Switch Collection Team
HAIR: Rush London
MAKE-UP: Goldwell Switch Collection Team
PHOTO: Courtesy of Goldwell

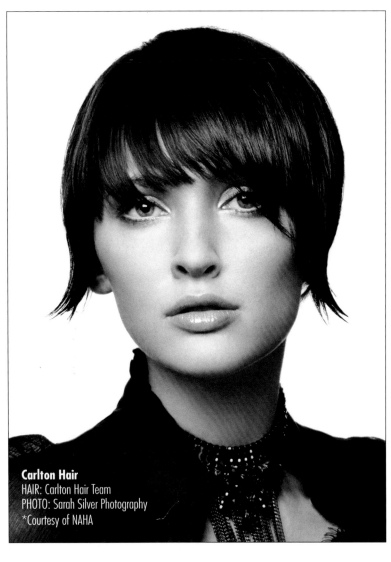

Carlton Hair
HAIR: Carlton Hair Team
PHOTO: Sarah Silver Photography
*Courtesy of NAHA

Carlton Hair
HAIR: Carlton Hair Team
PHOTO: Sarah Silver Photography
*Courtesy of NAHA

Carlton Hair
HAIR: Carlton Hair Team
PHOTO: Sarah Silver Photography
*Courtesy of NAHA

Primary Syn
HAIR: Anthony Marsalese
COLOR: James Simpson
PHOTO: Johnathon Roe

Goldwell

Goldwell

20

Pivot Point International-
The Netherlands
HAIR: Koenraad Engels
MAKE-UP: DINO
PHOTO: Mike van den Toom/David Placek

**Hair by Bennie
and Friends**
HAIR: Bennie Pollard
PHOTO: Edward Brown
*Courtesy of NAHA

Pivot Point International-Sweden
HAIR: Joakim Roos
MAKE-UP: Dino
PHOTO: Mike van den Toom/David Placek

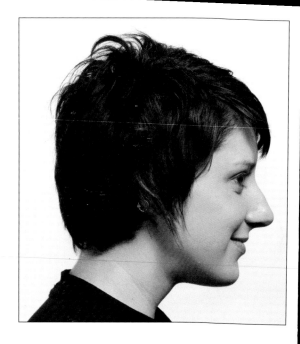

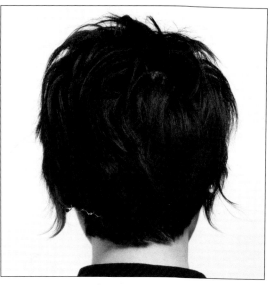

**Graham Webb International
Academy of Hair**
HAIR: Emillee Lauterbach
COLOR: Emillee Lauterbach
MAKE-UP: Katie Myers
PHOTO: Scott Bryant

John Amico Haircare & Jalyd Haircolor-The Salon
HAIR: Judy Petersen
COLOR: Judy Petersen
MAKE-UP: Susan Gnaidek
PHOTO: Scott Bryant

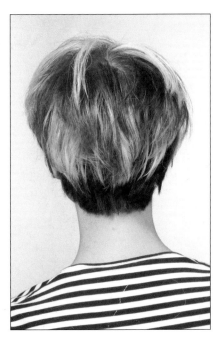

Joe's Salon & Spa
HAIR: Leighann Hynda
COLOR: Leighann Hynda
MAKE-UP: Sarah Griswold
PHOTO: John Kane

Transitions Salon
HAIR: Michelle Snedden
MAKE-UP: Cheryl Espostio
PHOTO: Jack Cutler

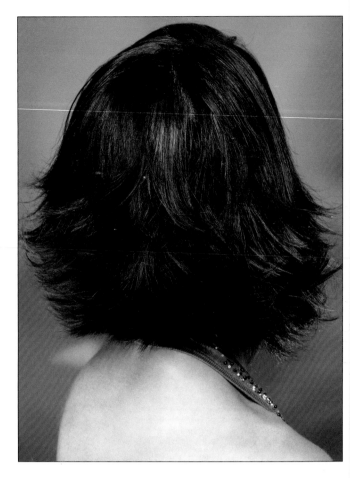

Salon: NV Ink
HAIR: Mary Fortinno
MAKE-UP: Mary Fortinno
PHOTO: Melissa Bergerstock N~Vision Photography

MEDIUM HAIR

Splash Hair Studio
HAIR: Marybeth Simpson
MAKE-UP: Cheryl Espostio
PHOTO: Jack Cutler

Shortino's Salon & Spa
HAIR: Shortino's Salon & Spa Team
MAKE-UP: Shortino's Salon & Spa Team
PHOTO: Tom Carson Photography

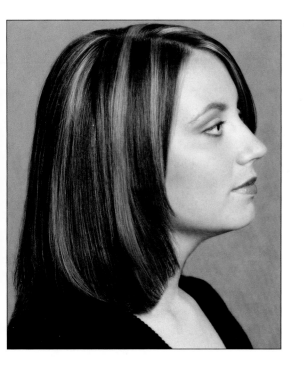

Salon Bella
HAIR: Regina Kling
MAKE-UP: Cheryl Espostio
PHOTO: Jack Cutler

Joe's Salon & Spa
HAIR: Charleen McILVenny Koval
MAKE-UP: Sarah Griswold
PHOTO: John Kane

Kathy Adams Salon
HAIR: Kathy Adams Salon Team
MAKE-UP: Kathy Adams Salon Team
PHOTO: Tom Carson Photography

**Sherif Zaki Salon &
The Oasis Spa**
HAIR: Sherif Zaki
COLOR: Courtney Turner
MAKE-UP: Elise Rowe
PHOTO: Scott Bryant

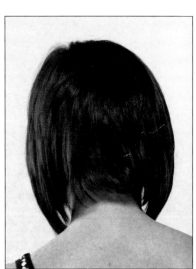

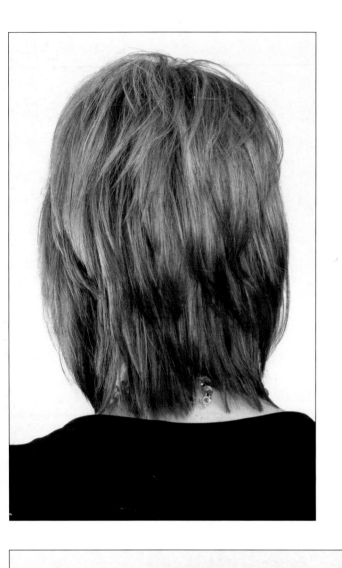

Jazlyn's Lady & Gent Salon
HAIR: Lana Hughes
MAKE-UP: Nico
PHOTO: Scott Bryant

Guy Anthony Salon
HAIR: Mado Nezry
MAKE-UP: Erique Lujan
PHOTO: Richard Viola

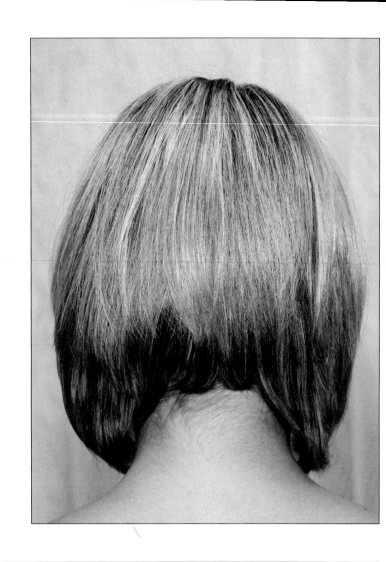

**Diadema
Hair Fashion**
HAIR: Diadema
MAKE-UP: Tiziana Romano for Diadema
PHOTO: Stefano Bidini

PON International-Anaheim Hills CA
HAIR: Mike Christianson
MAKE-UP: Jaime Queenin
PHOTO: Taggart Winterhalter for Purely Visual

MC College
HAIR: Lawna Gorham
PHOTO: Rhello Yorobe
*Courtesy of NAHA

Goldwell Switch Collection Team
HAIR: Rush London
MAKE-UP: Goldwell Switch Collection Team
PHOTO: Courtesy of Goldwell

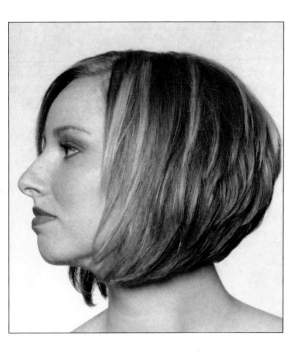

Karis Salon on Market St.
HAIR: Kristie Kuhns
MAKE-UP: Cheryl Espostio
PHOTO: Jack Cutler

LaDage Artistry
HAIR: Thomas LaDage
COLOR: Roy Sheefs
MAKE-UP: Thomas LaDage
PHOTO: Alissa Clark

Salon St. Germaine
HAIR: Po Mulholland
COLOR: Po Mulholland
MAKE-UP: Po Mulholland
PHOTO: Scott Bryant

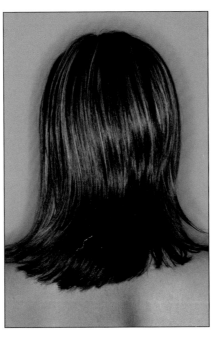

Sempre Bellezza Salon-Temecula CA
HAIR: Daniella Del Fante
MAKE-UP: Jaime Queenin
PHOTO: Taggart Winterhalter for Purely Visual

Kathy Adams Salon
HAIR: Kathy Adams Salon Team
MAKE-UP: Kathy Adams Salon Team
PHOTO: Tom Carson Photography

Sempre Bellezza
Salon-Temecula CA
HAIR: Daniella Del Fante
MAKE-UP: Jaime Queenin
PHOTO: Taggart Winterhalter
for Purely Visual

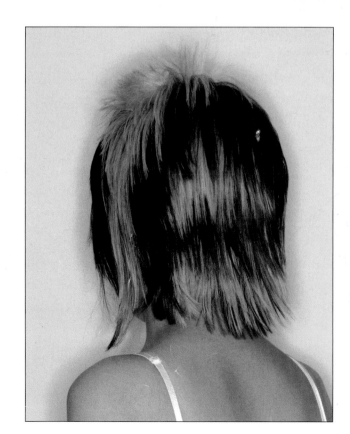

Salon De'Dawn
HAIR: Dawn Orlow-Townsend
MAKE-UP: Jaime Queenin
PHOTO: Taggart Winterhalter
for Purely Visual

Kathy Adams Salon
HAIR: Kathy Adams Salon Team
MAKE-UP: Kathy Adams Salon Team
PHOTO: Tom Carson Photography

**John Amico Haircare &
Jalyd Haircolor Top Reviews Salon**
HAIR: Lynne Villiaros
COLOR: Lynne Villiaros
MAKE-UP: Malia Villiaros
PHOTO: Scott Bryant

Joe's Salon & Spa
HAIR: Charleen McILVenny Koval
COLOR: Jennifer Barrett
MAKE-UP: Sarah Griswold
PHOTO: John Kane

Coiffure Hair Sun
HAIR: Hair Sun Team
MAKE-UP: Hair Sun Team
PHOTO: Uta W. Grutter

38

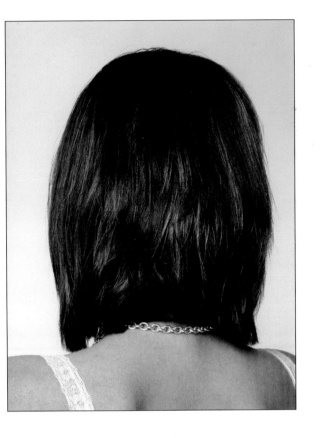

Fantastic Sams-Norco CA
HAIR: Marlena Victoria
PHOTO: Taggart Winterhalter
for Purely Visual

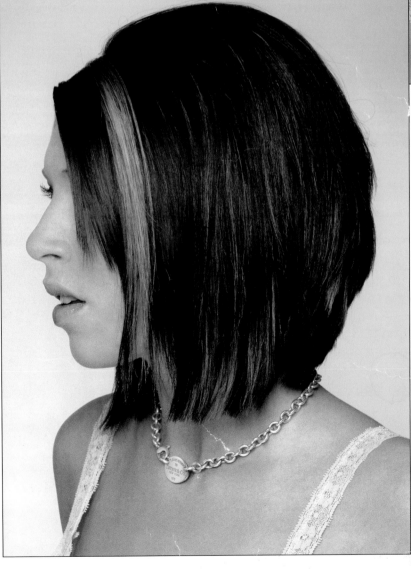

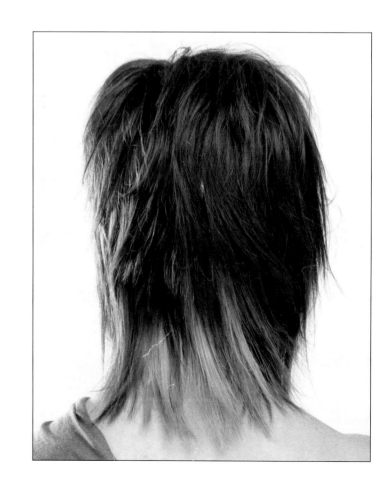

Hair Benders Internationale
HAIR: Angie Pilkington
COLOR: Angie Pilkington
MAKE-UP: Darin Wright
PHOTO: Scott Bryant

A Little Off the Top
HAIR: Sandee Lundby
MAKE-UP: Sandee Lundby
PHOTO: Jann Bloesser

**John Amico Haircare
& Jalyd Haircolor-
The Salon**
HAIR: Ron Anderson
COLOR: Ron Anderson
MAKE-UP: Sarah Laveille
PHOTO: Scott Bryant

Kathy Adams Salon
HAIR: Kathy Adams Salon Team
MAKE-UP: Kathy Adams Salon Team
PHOTO: Tom Carson Photography

Kathy Adams Salon
HAIR: Kathy Adams Salon Team
MAKE-UP: Kathy Adams Salon Team
PHOTO: Tom Carson Photography

Diadema Hair Fashion
HAIR: Diadema
MAKE-UP: Tiziana Romano for Diadema
PHOTO: Stefano Bidini

Paula's Design Team
HAIR: Paula Boldman
COLOR: Paula Boldman
MAKE-UP: Paula Boldman
PHOTO: Scott Bryant

Salon Bella
HAIR: Regina Kling
MAKE-UP: Cheryl Espostio
PHOTO: Jack Cutler

Scissorhand Station
HAIR: Susan Burkhardt
MAKE-UP: Cheryl Espostio
PHOTO: Jack Cutler

Salon Beauchesne & Je Beau International
HAIR: Julie Beauchesne
MAKE-UP: Julie Beauchesne
PHOTO: Tom Carson

The Loft Salon
HAIR: Ann Marie Walts
MAKE-UP: Ann Marie Walts
PHOTO: Tim Kendrick - Steinmetz Photography

Diadema Hair Fashion
HAIR: Diadema
MAKE-UP: Tiziana Romano
for Diadema
PHOTO: Stefano Bidini

Diadema Hair Fashion
HAIR: Diadema
MAKE-UP: Tiziana Romano
for Diadema
PHOTO: Stefano Bidini

La Petite Salon
HAIR: Brian Asper
MAKE-UP: Cheryl Espostio
PHOTO: Jack Cutler

Diadema Hair Fashion
HAIR: Diadema
MAKE-UP: Tiziana Romano
for Diadema
PHOTO: Stefano Bidini

47

Gina Khan Salon
HAIR: Gina Khan
PHOTO: Vijai Manilal

Gina Khan Salon
HAIR: Gina Khan
PHOTO: Vijai Manilal

Transitions Salon
HAIR: Michelle Snedden
MAKE-UP: Cheryl Espostio
PHOTO: Jack Cutler

**Graham Webb International
Academy of Hair**
HAIR: Amethyst Chapple
COLOR: Amethyst Chapple
MAKE-UP: Mary Toman
PHOTO: Scott Bryant

Elie.Elie Salon
HAIR: Barbara Lhotan
COLOR: Barbara Lhotan
MAKE-UP: Brandon Russell
PHOTO: Scott Bryant

Kathy Adams Salon
HAIR: Kathy Adams Salon Team
MAKE-UP: Kathy Adams Salon Team
PHOTO: Tom Carson Photography

Kathy Adams Salon
HAIR: Kathy Adams Salon Team
MAKE-UP: Kathy Adams Salon Team
PHOTO: Tom Carson Photography

Kathy Adams Salon
HAIR: Kathy Adams Salon Team
MAKE-UP: Kathy Adams Salon Team
PHOTO: Tom Carson Photography

John Amico Haircare & Jalyd
Haircolor-The Salon
HAIR: Ron Anderson
COLOR: Melissa Henig
MAKE-UP: Mark Schmudde
PHOTO: Scott Bryant

John Amico Haircare
& Jalyd Haircolor-
Paula's Design Team
HAIR: Eric Williams
COLOR: Eric Williams
MAKE-UP: Brandy Long
PHOTO: Scott Bryant

Fantastic Sams-Culver City CA
HAIR: Rashidah Thomas Eady
PHOTO: Taggart Winterhalter for
Purely Visual

...dwell Trend Zoom
... Goldwell Trend Zoom Team
...-UP: Goldwell Trend Zoom Team
...O: Courtesy of Goldwell

LONG HAIR

HAIR: Kathy Adams Salon Team
MAKE-UP: Kathy Adams Salon Team
PHOTO: Tom Carson Photography

**John Amico Haircare & Jalyd
Haircolor-The Glitterati Salon**
HAIR: Marga Perkins
COLOR: Marga Perkins
MAKE-UP: Marga Perkins
PHOTO: Scott Bryant

Reflections Of You Salon & Spa
HAIR: Reflections Of You Team
COLOR: Reflections Of You Team
MAKE-UP: Reflections Of You Team
PHOTO: Scott Bryant

John Amico Haircare & Jalyd
Haircolor-Paula's Design Team
HAIR: Eli Raley
COLOR: Eli Raley
MAKE-UP: Brandy Long
PHOTO: Scott Bryant

Mason & Friends Salon
HAIR: Julie Sperty
COLOR: Julie Sperty
MAKE-UP: Julie Sperty
PHOTO: Scott Bryant

Mane Street
HAIR: Anne Nicole
PHOTO: Robert Holmes
Shooting Stars

Shortino's Salon & Spa
HAIR: Shortino's Salon & Spa Team
MAKE-UP: Shortino's Salon & Spa Team
PHOTO: Tom Carson Photography

Kathy Adams Salon
HAIR: Kathy Adams Salon Team
MAKE-UP: Kathy Adams Salon Team
PHOTO: Tom Carson Photography

Kathy Adams Salon
HAIR: Kathy Adams Salon Team
MAKE-UP: Kathy Adams Salon Team
PHOTO: Tom Carson Photography

Profiles Hair Salon
HAIR: Carmela Scarlato
MAKE-UP: Connie Geier
PHOTO:
www.BillMcKenna.com

Kathy Adams Salon
HAIR: Kathy Adams Salon Team
MAKE-UP: Kathy Adams Salon Team
PHOTO: Tom Carson Photography

Kathy Adams Salon
HAIR: Kathy Adams Salon Team
MAKE-UP: Kathy Adams Salon Team
PHOTO: Tom Carson Photography

Ellen Barkin
PHOTO: Lawrence Lucier/FilmMagic.com

Patricia Heaton
PHOTO: Jeffrey Mayer/WireImage.com

Lauren Holly
PHOTO: John Kopaloff/FilmMagic.com

Heather Locklear
PHOTO: Jeffrey Mayer/WireImage.com

62

Cheryl Ladd
PHOTO: John Sciulli/WireImage.com

Marg Helgenberger
PHOTO: Kevin Mazur/WireImage.com

Allison Janney
PHOTO: Steve Granitz/WireImage.com

Loni Anderson
PHOTO: Gregg DeGuire/WireImage.com

Patricia Arquette
PHOTO: Jeff Kravitz/Variety via FilmMagic.com

Tatum O'Neal
PHOTO: Michael Loccisano/FilmMagic.com

Christie Brinkley
PHOTO: Stephen Lovekin/WireImage.com

Suzanne Sommers
PHOTO: John Kopaloff/FilmMagic.com

Susan Lucci
PHOTO: Kevin Mazur/WireImage.com

Clair Danes
PHOTO: Lester Cohen/Variety via WireImage.com

Victoria Beckham
PHOTO: Eammon McCormack/WireImage.com

Sandra Bullock
PHOTO: Dimitrios Kambouris/WireImage.com

Julia Louis-Dreyfuss
PHOTO: Gregg DeGuire/WireImage.com

Elisabeth Shue
PHOTO: Michael Tran/FilmMagic.com

Jenny McCarthy
PHOTO: Jon Kopaloff/FilmMagic.com

Dorothy Hamill
PHOTO: Gregg DeGuire/WireImage.com

Sharon Lawrence
PHOTO: Michael Bezjian/WireImage.com

Reba McEntire
PHOTO: Dan Steinberg/
FilmMagic.com

Jodie Foster
PHOTO: John Shearer/WireImage.com

Ellen Degeneres
PHOTO: Gregg DeGuire/WireImage.com

Cheryl Hines
PHOTO: Jeffrey Mayer/
WireImage.com

THE CINEMA GQ

Julianna Moore
PHOTO: Jamie McCarthy/WireImage.com

Sarah Ferguson
PHOTO: Marc Von Holden/WireImage.com

Anne Heche
PHOTO: John Kopaloff/FilmMagic.com

Katie Holmes
PHOTO: WireImage.comJim Spellman/WireImage.com

Candice Bergen
PHOTO: Albert O. Ortega/WireImage.com

Florence Henderson
Photo: Todd Williamson/
WireImage.com

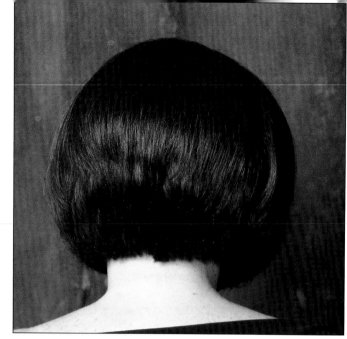

Artistic Hair
HAIR: Marlene Jackson
MAKE-UP: Jaime Queenin
PHOTO: Taggart Winterhalter
for Purely Visual

T.Carltons Studio
HAIR: Danielle Otero
MAKE-UP: T.Carltons
PHOTO: Larry Hacken

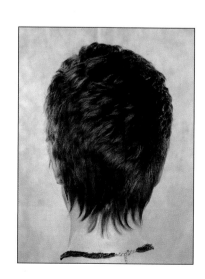

Artistic Hair
HAIR: Barbara Nolasco
MAKE-UP: Sara Wayne
PHOTO: Taggart Winterhalter for Purely Visual

T.Carltons Studio
HAIR: Christine Frankie
MAKE-UP: T.Carltons
PHOTO: Larry Hacken

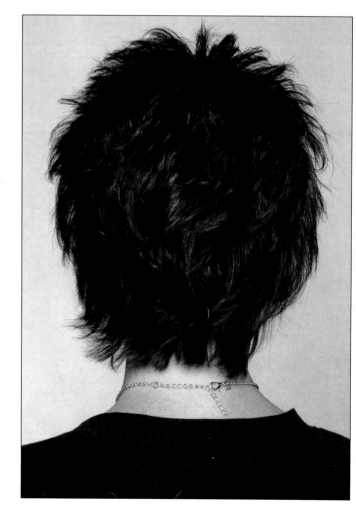

Fantastic Sams-Foothill Ranch CA
HAIR: Jennifer Pecbot
PHOTO: Taggart Winterhalter for Purely Visual

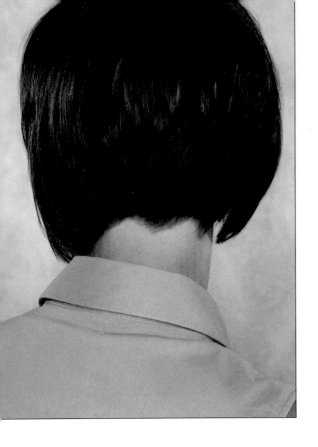

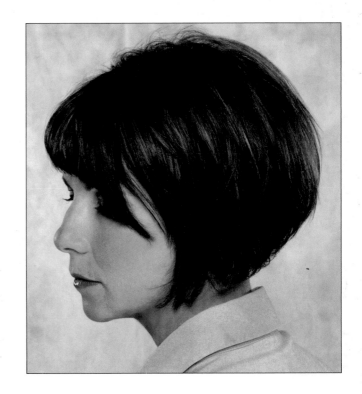

Carter T. Lund & Associates
HAIR: Carter T. Lund
MAKE-UP: Jaime Queenin
PHOTO: Taggart Winterhalter for Purely Visual

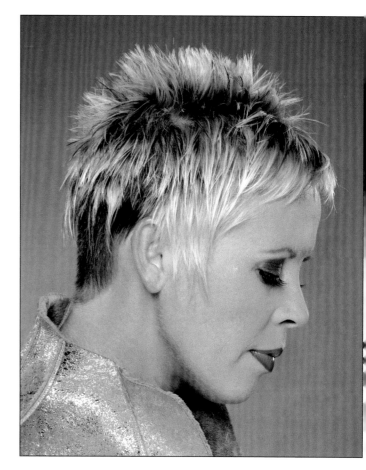

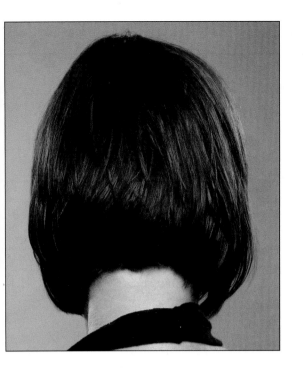

Salon Boucle
HAIR: Stephanie Clinton
MAKE-UP: Sara Wayne
PHOTO: Taggart Winterhalter
for Purely Visual

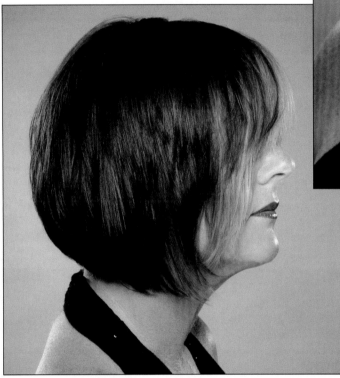

Salon Boucle
HAIR: Stephanie Clinton
MAKE-UP: Jaime Queenin
PHOTO: Taggart Winterhalter
for Purely Visual

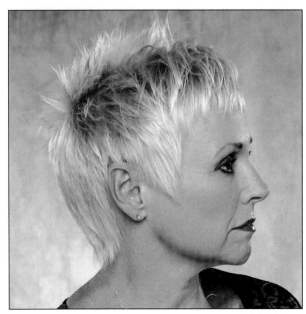

Fantastic Sams-Foothill Ranch CA
HAIR: Charles Holdeman
PHOTO: Taggart Winterhalter
for Purely Visual

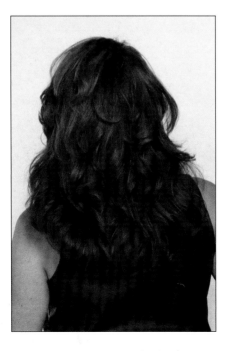

Salon Tekniques
HAIR: Marissa Toth
COLOR: Marissa Toth
MAKE-UP: Marissa Toth
PHOTO: Scott Bryant

Hair Benders Internationalé
HAIR: Hair Benders Design Team
COLOR: Hair Benders Design Team
MAKE-UP: Darin Wright
PHOTO: Scott Bryant

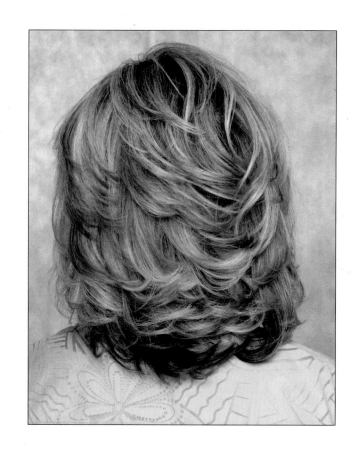

Salon Boucle
HAIR: Tammy Reindl
MAKE-UP: Sara Wayne
PHOTO: Taggart Winterhalter
for Purely Visual

TressAllure
HAIR: Alan Eaton

TressAllure

TressAllure

TressAllure

TressAllure
HAIR: Alan Eaton

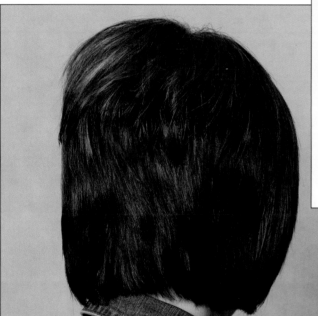

Twist for Hair Skin & Nails
HAIR: Chellis R. Derr
MAKE-UP: Cheryl Espostio
PHOTO: Jack Cutler

Fantastic Sams-Brea CA
HAIR: Toni Naisbitt
PHOTO: Taggart Winterhalter for
Purely Visual

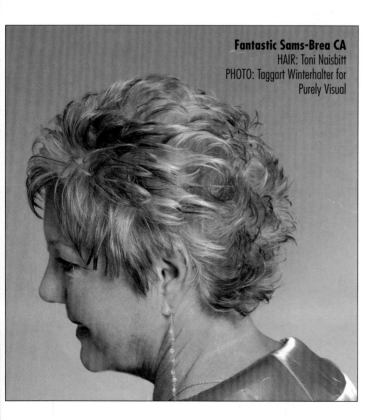

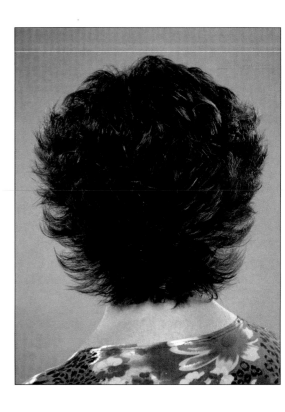

Salon: Piccasso's Colour Studio
HAIR: Cynthia Bleier
MAKE-UP: Jaime Queenin
PHOTO: Taggart Winterhalter for Purely Visual

Kathy Adams Salon
HAIR: Kathy Adams Salon Team
MAKE-UP: Kathy Adams Salon Team
PHOTO: Tom Carson Photography

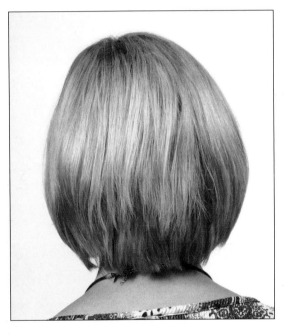

**John Amico Haircare &
Jalyd Haircolor-The Salon**
HAIR: Susan Gnaidek
MAKE-UP: Mark Schmudde
PHOTO: Scott Bryant

Hair Benders Internationalé
HAIR: Hair Benders Design Team
COLOR: Hair Benders Design Team
MAKE-UP: Darin Wright
PHOTO: Scott Bryant

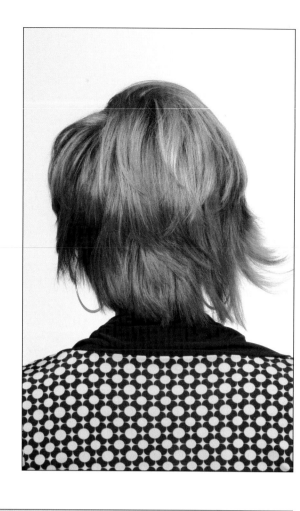

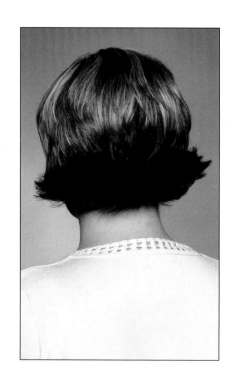

Fantastic Sams-Lake Elsinore CA
HAIR: Rosalia Guana
PHOTO: Taggart Winterhalter
for Purely Visual

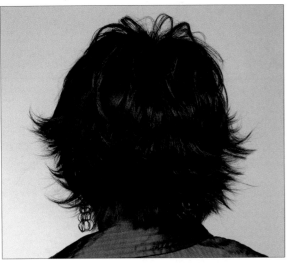

Fantastic Sams-Corona CA
HAIR: Jennifer M. Jaques
PHOTO: Taggart Winterhalter
for Purely Visual

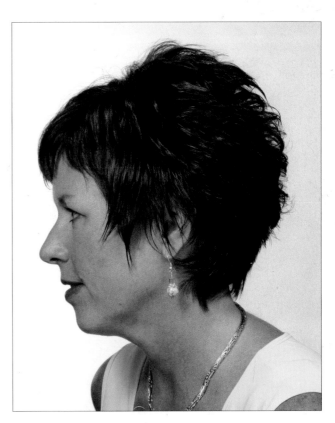

**John Amico Haircare &
Jalyd Haircolor-The Salon**
HAIR: Ron Anderson
COLOR: Ron Anderson
MAKE-UP: Cathy Lepczynski
PHOTO: Scott Bryant

T.Carltons Studio
HAIR: Hieu Truong
MAKE-UP: T.Carltons
PHOTO: Larry Hacken

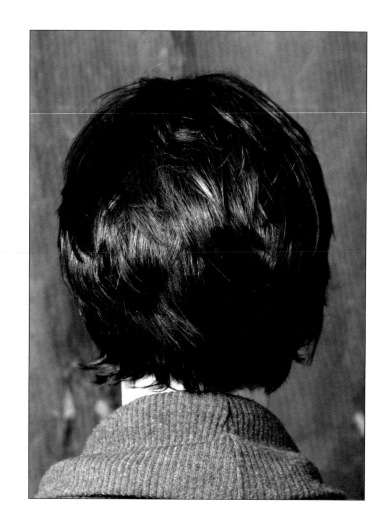

Shag
HAIR: William Trotter
MAKE-UP: Cheryl Espostio
PHOTO: Jack Cutler

TressAllure

TressAllure
HAIR: Alan Eaton

TressAllure

TressAllure
HAIR: Alan Eaton

Élan Hair Designs
HAIR: Penelopi Koutras
MAKE-UP: Jeanette Beck
PHOTO: Michael McWeeney

Wilborn Hair Co
HAIR: Megan Hastings
MAKE-UP: Megan Hastings
PHOTO: Gavin Peters

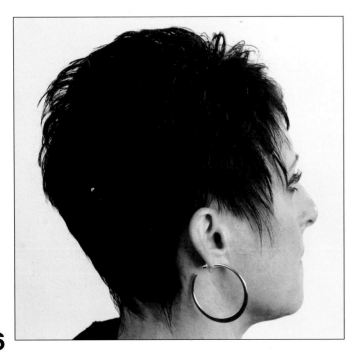

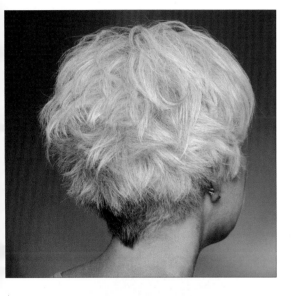

NV Ink
HAIR: Mary Fortinno
MAKE-UP: Mary Fortinno
PHOTO: Melissa Bergerstock N~Vision Photography

Michael's Salon & Day Spa
HAIR: Alesha Norbeck
COLOR: Alesha Norbeck
MAKE-UP: Paula Piersail
PHOTO: Scott Bryant

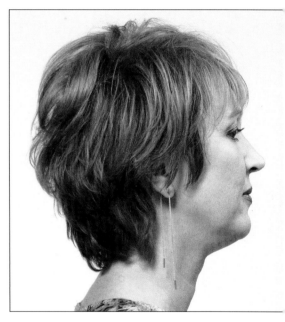

Planet Cosmo Salon
HAIR: Nora Giuliani
MAKE-UP: Cosmo Easterly
PHOTO: Joolsphoto.com

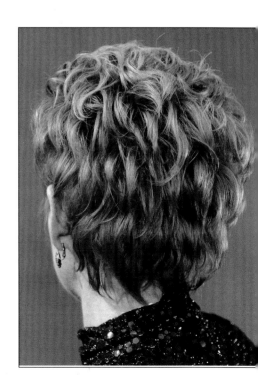

Three Small Rooms
HAIR: Suzanne Martin
PHOTO: Babak
*Courtesy of NAHA

Gina Khan Salon
HAIR: Gina Khan
PHOTO: Vijai Manilal

Gina Khan Salon
HAIR: Gina Khan
PHOTO: Vijai Manilal

Alexander's Grand Salon & Spa
HAIR: Dana Corbitt
MAKE-UP: Monica Guzman
PHOTO: Taggart Winterhalter for Purely Visual

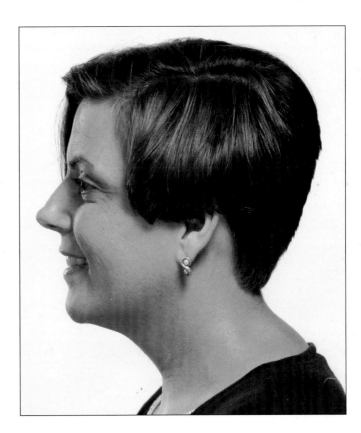

Amir Salon
HAIR: Amir H. Gilanshah
COLOR: Amir H. Gilanshah
MAKE-UP: Reneé
PHOTO: Scott Bryant

Shortino's Salon & Spa
HAIR: Shortino's Salon & Spa Team
MAKE-UP: Shortino's Salon & Spa Team
PHOTO: Tom Carson Photography

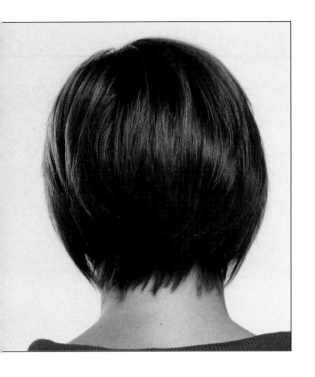

Mason & Friends Salon
HAIR: Rebecca Davis
COLOR: Rebecca Davis
MAKE-UP: Rebecca Davis
PHOTO: Scott Bryant

**John Amico Haircare & Jalyd Haircolor-
Parkview Shear Perfection**
HAIR: Rhonda Murphy
COLOR: Rhonda Murphy
MAKE-UP: Rhonda Murphy
PHOTO: Scott Bryant

Salon Boucle
HAIR: Tammy Reindl
MAKE-UP: Jaime Queenin
PHOTO: Taggart Winterhalter
for Purely Visual

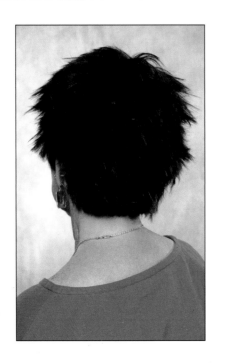

Fletcher/Smith the Spa
HAIR: Todd Snow
MAKE-UP: Sara Wayne
PHOTO: Taggart Winterhalter
for Purely Visual

Salon Tekniques
HAIR: Patti Meade
COLOR: Patti Meade
MAKE-UP: Patti Meade
PHOTO: Scott Bryant

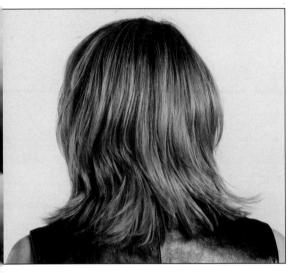

**John Amico Haircare
& Jalyd Haircolor-
David the Salon**
HAIR: Abigail Sickman
COLOE: Abigail Sickman
MAKE-UP: Abigail Sickman
PHOTO: Scott Bryant

SOPHISTICATED STYLES

95

*Courtesy of NAHA-North American Hairstyling Awards

Publisher/CEO: Deborah Carver • Managing Director: Sheryl Lenzkes • Art Director: Michael Block • Photo Coordinator: Mara Soldinger

To Contact Us: Creative Age Communications • 7628 Densmore Avenue, Van Nuys, California 91406-2042 • PH 800.634.8500 • FAX 818.782.7450

Interested in getting published . . . go to inspirebooks.com to download submission forms and information